T0084441

EULENBURG AUDIO+SCORE

Ludwig van Beethoven

Symphony No. 7 in A major / A-Dur

Op. 92

Edited by / Herausgegeben von
Richard Clarke

EULENBURG

EAS 175
ISBN 978-3-7957-6570-5
ISMN 979-0-2002-2565-5

Ernst Eulenburg Ltd
48 Great Marlborough Street
London W1F 7BB

Contents / Inhalt

IV.   Allegro con brio

Preface

Dedicated to Count Moritz von Fries
Composed: Autumn 1811 to June 1812 in Vienna
First performance: 8 December 1813 in Vienna
Original publisher: S.A.Steiner & Co., Vienna, 1816
Instrumentation: 2 Flutes, 2 Oboes, 2 Clarinets, 2 Bassoons – 2 Horns,
2 Trumpets – Timpani – Strings
Duration: ca. 37 minutes

For most of his adult life, Beethoven was tormented by ill health. Quite apart from his famous deafness, he suffered from persistent ringing in the ears (tinnitus), headaches, abdominal disorders, severe constipation, rheumatic attacks and a whole host of more mysterious ailments. He was also prone to serious depression – not surprisingly perhaps, considering the pain and frustration that he endured. And yet he clearly had tremendous reserves of strength, both physical and mental, fighting off infections and rising above all manner of other tribulations. Sometimes it was the very act of working that saved him from despair – as Beethoven himself acknowledged in his famous private confession, the so-called *Heiligenstadt Testament*, dated 6–10 October 1802. At other times the experience of recovery gave new impetus to composition.

It was during just such a period of recuperation that Beethoven wrote his Seventh Symphony. In 1811, the prominent Viennese physician, Dr Giovanni Malfatti, recommended that Beethoven spend the summer in the Bohemian spa-town of Teplitz, famous for its 'cure'. It was one of the few pieces of good medical advice that Beethoven ever received. Teplitz was also a place of relative peace in troubled times. During the Napoleonic wars, diplomats from all sides met there, regarding it as neutral territory. The visit obviously gave Beethoven a personal and artistic boost, as he returned to Vienna with plans for two symphonies. He began writing the Seventh almost immediately, while making notes about 'a second symphony in D minor'. The latter did not fully materialise until 12 years later, as the choral Ninth Symphony; but as soon as Beethoven had finished No.7, in May 1812, he began work on the equally buoyant Eighth. Whatever else he may have been suffering from at this time, there was clearly no shortage of creative energy.

Granted, one should always resist drawing direct comparisons between Beethoven's presumed emotional state and the character of the music that he produced at that particular time. When Beethoven wrote that despairing *Heiligenstadt Testament* in the autumn of 1802 he was also working on his Second Symphony – a work not without its abrasive moments but, most commentators would agree, one that is ultimately positive and full of vitality throughout. It is difficult, however, to avoid the feeling that Beethoven's renewed dynamism after his stay in Teplitz found direct expression in his Seventh Symphony – the symphony Wagner famously described as 'the apotheosis of the dance'. The sheer physical energy of the work, expressed in bracing muscular rhythms and brilliant orchestration, can, in some performances, border on the unnerving. Confronted with one of the symphony's many obsessively repeating passages (possibly the final build-up in the first movement, bb401ff), Beethoven's younger contemporary Carl Maria von Weber pronounced him 'ripe for the madhouse'. There are darker, destabilizing elements, expressed in the symphony's recurring tendency to lean towards the relatively remote keys of C and F major (see for instance the two statements of the woodwind theme beginning at bb23 and 42 in the first movement introduction). Yet at the close of the finale the home key of A major re-emerges in full splendour, reinforced by two massive cadential passages, both marked *fff* (bb427 and 443) – one of the earliest examples of such an extreme dynamic in music.

In the introduction to the first movement there seems to be little of the dance about the Seventh Symphony. Slow woodwind phrases are brusquely punctuated by chords from the full orchestra, but then faster string figures galvanize the music into physical action (b10f). Eventually this relatively slow introduction settles on a single note – an E, repeated by alternating woodwind and strings (b53f). This soon develops into a sprightly dotted rhythm, and the *Vivace* begins. This dotted rhythm – basically an emphatic long note followed by two short ones (in poetic metrical terms, a 'dactyl') – not only dominates this first movement, but plays a crucial part in the other three movements as well. It is also present (in a slightly different form) in the main theme of the following *Allegretto* (bb3–4ff), after the initial minor key wind chord calls us to attention. This magically atmospheric movement was such a success at its first performance that it had to be repeated. It made a great impression on the young Schubert also, who echoed its measured, but strangely weightless tread in a number of his later works.

After the *Allegretto*, the *Presto* bursts into life. This has all the racing forward momentum of a typical Beethoven Scherzo. It is twice interrupted by a slower Trio section (with another version of the long-short-short rhythmic pattern in its main theme), and yet its vitality seems irrepressible: a third, more tentative attempt to establish the slower Trio theme (b645f) is magnificently dismissed by five crisp orchestral chords. The Scherzo is, however, in the 'wrong' key: the destabilizing F major. It is now the finale's task to ram home the symphony's tonic key, A major. It duly begins with a massive assertion of the note E, the dominant of A major, which continues emphatically in the bass almost throughout the first phase of the main theme (bb5–12). The movement develops into a magnificent bacchanal, pounding almost to a frenzy at the symphony's seminal long-short-short rhythmic pattern. The coda veers dangerously towards F for the last time (b377f), now felt as the dominant of B flat major; but at last the bass F falls to a far more rational E (b384f), and a huge *crescendo* on a reinforced dominant pedal begins (b389). The last thing we hear, in the final three bars, is the Seventh Symphony's basic dactylic rhythm, twice, fused triumphantly with the home triad, A major.

Stephen Johnson

Vorwort

dem Grafen Moritz von Fries gewidmet
komponiert: Herbst 1811 bis Juni 1812 in Wien
Uraufführung: 8. Dezember 1813 in Wien
Originalverlag: S. A. Steiner & Co., Wien, 1816
Orchesterbesetzung: 2 Flöten, 2 Oboen, 2 Klarinetten, 2 Fagotte –
2 Hörner, 2 Trompeten – Pauken – Streicher
Spieldauer: etwa 37 Minuten

Fast sein ganzes Erwachsenenleben hindurch wurde Beethoven von seiner schlechten Gesundheit gepeinigt. Ganz abgesehen von seiner allseits bekannten Taubheit, litt er unter Tinnitus, Kopfschmerzen, Unterleibsbeschwerden, schwerwiegender Darmträgheit, rheumatischen Anfällen und einer ganzen Menge anderer, rätselhafter Gebrechen. Zudem war er anfällig für schwere Depressionen – was wenig überraschend erscheinen mag in Anbetracht des Schmerzes und der Enttäuschungen, die er ertrug. Und dennoch verfügte er über enorme physische als auch psychische Kraftreserven, um Infektionen abzuwehren und über jegliche Art von Trübsal erhaben zu sein. Manchmal war es der bloße Arbeitsprozess, der ihn vor der Verzweiflung bewahrte – wie Beethoven selbst in seiner berühmten privaten Beichte, dem so genannten *Heiligenstädter Testament*, 6.–10. Oktober 1802, bemerkte. Zu anderen Zeiten gab das Gefühl der Genesung neuen Anstoß zum Komponieren.

Seine 7. Sinfonie schrieb Beethoven genau während solch einer Phase der Erholung. Der berühmte Wiener Arzt Dr. Giovanni Malfatti hatte Beethoven 1811 empfohlen, den Sommer in dem bekannten böhmischen Kurort Teplitz zu verbringen. Es war einer der wenigen guten medizinischen Ratschläge, die Beethoven jemals erhielt. Außerdem war Teplitz ein Ort der relativen Ruhe in unruhigen Zeiten. Während der Napoleonischen Kriege war es ein Treffpunkt der Diplomaten, die es als neutrales Territorium ansahen. Da Beethoven mit Plänen für zwei neue Sinfonien nach Wien zurückkehrte, hatte ihm der Besuch offensichtlich persönlich und künstlerisch neuen Antrieb gegeben. Fast unmittelbar begann er die „Siebte" zu schreiben, während er gleichzeitig Notizen über eine zweite Sinfonie in d-Moll machte. Letztere sollte erst 12 Jahre später – als 9. Sinfonie – zustande kommen. Aber sobald Beethoven im Mai 1812 die 7. Sinfonie beendet hatte, nahm er die Arbeit zu der gleichermaßen heiteren „Achten" auf. Woran auch immer er zu dieser Zeit gelitten haben mag, beschnitt es jedenfalls nicht seine kreative Energie.

Zugegebenermaßen, man sollte sich immer vorsehen, direkte Vergleiche zwischen Beethovens mutmaßlicher emotionaler Verfassung und dem Charakter der in diesem Moment geschaffenen Musik zu ziehen. Als Beethoven im Herbst 1802 das verzweifelte *Heiligenstäd-*

ter Testament schrieb, arbeitete er zugleich auch an seiner 2. Sinfonie, eine Komposition, die nicht frei von ruppigen Stellen ist, aber – und hier würden wohl die meisten Kommentatoren zustimmen – letztlich positiv und durchweg reich an Lebensfreude. Man kann sich dennoch nur schwer dem Gefühl entziehen, dass Beethovens erneuerte Energie nach seinem Aufenthalt in Teplitz direkten Eingang in die 7. Sinfonie gefunden hat – die Sinfonie, die Wagner bekanntlich als „Apotheose des Tanzes" bezeichnet hatte. Die schier physische Kraft der spannungsgeladenen Rhythmen und der brillanten Orchestrierung kann für den Zuhörer – in einigen Aufführungen – an das Enervierende grenzen. Als Beethovens jüngerer Zeitgenosse Carl Maria von Weber einmal mit einem der sich wie besessen wiederholenden Abschnitte der Sinfonie (möglicherweise das finale Aufbäumen im ersten Satz, T. 401ff.) konfrontiert wurde, erklärte er ihn „reif für das Irrenhaus". Es gibt dunklere, destabilisierende Elemente, so die wiederkehrende Tendenz in Richtung der relativ entfernten Tonarten C- und F-Dur (siehe beispielsweise die beiden Ausführungen des Holzbläser-Themas in der Einleitung des ersten Satzes, beginnend in den Takten 23 und 42). Dennoch tritt die Grundtonart A-Dur zum Abschluss des Finales wieder in voller Pracht hervor, verstärkt durch zwei gewaltige kadenzielle Passagen (T. 427 und 443), die beide mit *fff* bezeichnet sind – eines der frühesten Beispiele solch einer extremen Dynamik in der Musik.

In der Einleitung des ersten Satzes scheint die 7. Symphonie nur wenig Tänzerisches zu haben. Langsame Holzbläserphrasen werden von Akkorden des ganzen Orchesters schroff unterbrochen, aber dann drängen die schnelleren Streicherfiguren die Musik zu physischer Aktivität (T. 10f.). Letztendlich mündet diese relativ langsame Einleitung in einer einzigen gemeinsamen Note – einem E, das abwechselnd von Holzbläsern und Streichern wiederholt wird (T. 53f.). Bald entwickelt sich daraus ein lebhafter punktierter Rhythmus, und das Vivace beginnt. Dieser punktierte Rhythmus – grundsätzlich eine betont lange Note, gefolgt von zwei kurzen (gleichbedeutend mit dem Versmaß Daktylus in der Dichtung) – dominiert nicht nur den ersten Satz, sondern spielt auch in den anderen drei Sätzen eine entscheidende Rolle. Auch im Hauptthema des folgenden Allegretto (T. 3–4ff.) ist es – in leicht veränderter Form – gegenwärtig, nachdem der anfängliche Moll-Akkord der Holzbläser unsere Aufmerksamkeit erregt hat. Dieser zauberhaft stimmungsvolle Satz war bei seiner Uraufführung solch ein Erfolg, dass er wiederholt werden musste. Auch beim jungen Schubert, der diese getragene und doch seltsam schwerelose Anmutung in etlichen späteren Werken wiederholte, hinterließ er großen Eindruck.

Nach dem Allegretto bricht das Presto hervor, das den ganzen vorwärts drängenden Schwung eines Beethoven-Scherzos in sich trägt. Zweimal wird es unterbrochen von einem langsameren Trio-Abschnitt (mit einer weiteren Version des rhythmischen Musters lang-kurz-kurz im Hauptthema), und dennoch scheint seine Lebensfreude unbezähmbar; ein dritter, eher zögerlicher Versuch das langsame Trio-Thema aufzubauen (T. 645f.) wird auf großartige Weise von fünf forschen Orchesterakkorden zurückgewiesen. Das Scherzo steht allerdings in der „falschen" Tonart: dem destabilisierenden F-Dur. Nun ist es Aufgabe des Finales, zur Grundtonart der Sinfonie, A-Dur, zurückzuführen. Ordnungsgemäß beginnt es mit einem massiven Insistieren auf der Note E, der Dominante von A-Dur, das fast den ganzen ersten Abschnitt des Hauptthemas (T. 5–12) hindurch nachdrücklich im Bass wiederholt wird. Der Satz entwickelt sich zu einem herrlichen Bacchanal, indem der Grundrhythmus der Sinfonie, lang-kurz-kurz, fast bis zur Ekstase getrieben wird. Die Coda schert zum letzten Mal gefährlich zu F-Dur aus (T. 377f.), das man nun als Dominante von B-Dur empfindet. Aber zuletzt fällt das F im Bass zum vernünftigeren E-Dur (T. 384f.), und ein gewaltiges *crescendo* beginnt auf einem verstärkten Dominant-Pedalklang (T. 389). Das Letzte, was wir in den drei finalen Takten hören, ist der zweimal wiederholte, daktylische Grundrhythmus der 7. Sinfonie, vereinigt mit dem Dreiklang der Grundtonart A-Dur.

Stephen Johnson
Übersetzung: Sandra Borzikowski

Symphony No. 7

Dem Hochgeborenen Herrn Moritz Reichsgrafen von Fries
Sr. k. k. apost. Majestät wirklichen Kämmerer &&& in Erfurt gewidmet

Ludwig van Beethoven
(1770–1827)
Op. 92

I. **Poco sostenuto** ($\quad$ = 69)

EAS 175

Edited by Richard Clarke
© 2011 Ernst Eulenburg Ltd, London
and Ernst Eulenburg & Co GmbH, Mainz

2

3

4

Vivace (♩. = 104)

8

12

14

15

EAS 175

23

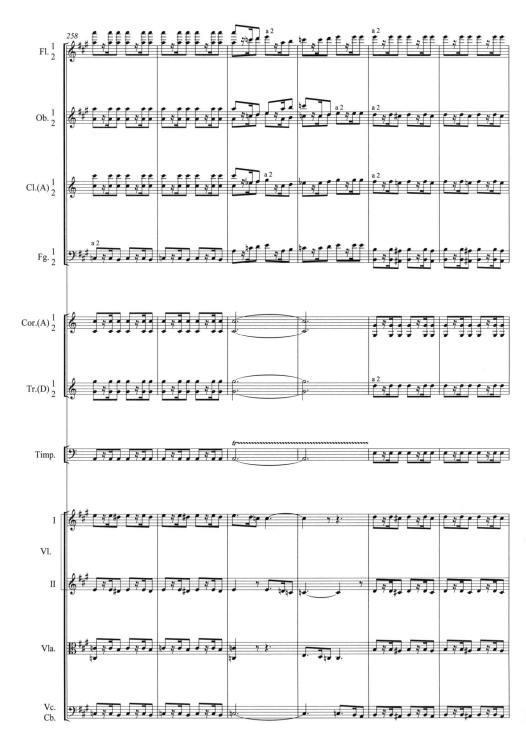

28

32

33

EAS 175

II. Allegretto (♩ = 76)

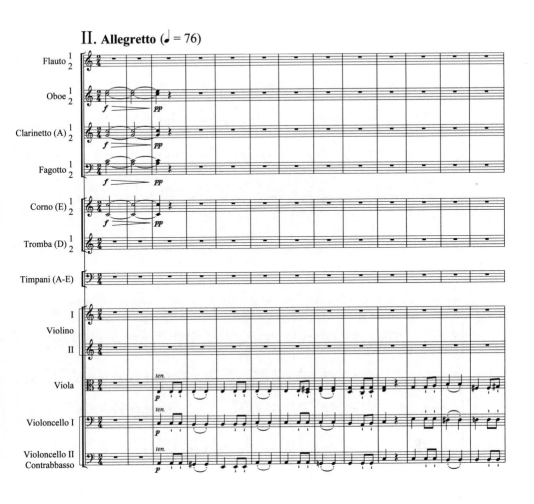

42

44

48

50

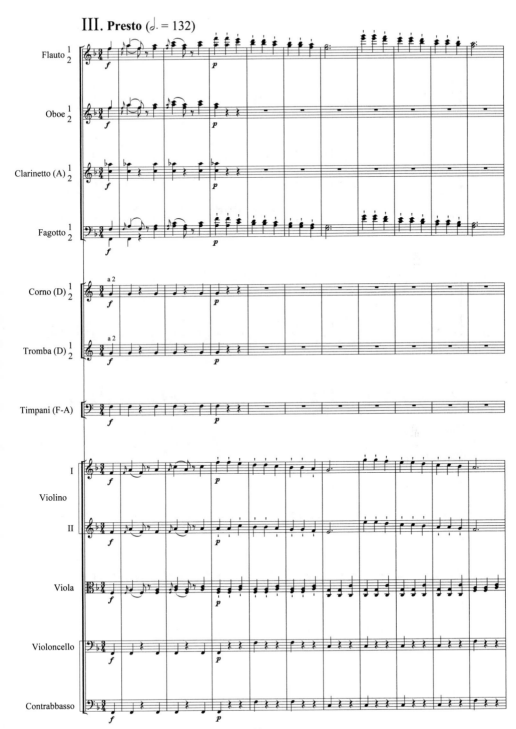

58

60

EAS 175

64

68

Assai meno presto

78

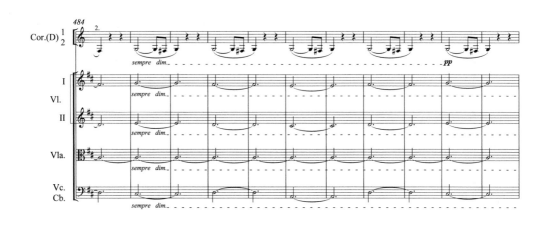

86

IV. **Allegro con brio** ($\textbf{.} = 72$)

90

94

98

99

EAS 175

104

EAS 175

106

EAS 175

108

EAS 175

110

EAS 175

114

Printed in China